DOVES AND

CHRISTINA ROSSETTI

Doves and Pomegranates

Poems for young readers chosen by
David Powell

Introduced by
Naomi Lewis

ILLUSTRATED BY
Margery Gill

THE BODLEY HEAD
LONDON SYDNEY
TORONTO

OTHER POETRY SELECTIONS
FOR YOUNG READERS

William Blake: *A Grain of Sand*

Edmund Blunden: *The Midnight Skaters*

John Clare: *The Wood is Sweet*

Emily Dickinson: *A Letter to the World*

Robert Frost: *You Come Too*

Robert Herrick: *The Music of a Feast*

Edward Thomas: *The Green Roads*

SBN 370 01251 8
This selection © David Powell 1969
Foreword © The Bodley Head Ltd 1969
Illustrations © The Bodley Head Ltd 1969
Printed and bound in Great Britain for
The Bodley Head Ltd
9 Bow Street, London WC2
by W & J Mackay & Co Ltd, Chatham
Set in 'Monotype' Baskerville
This selection first published 1969

Introduction by

NAOMI LEWIS

No one can doubt that women were writing (or making) poetry at all times in England's historied past. But for various social reasons, only a very few of them—and these were usually titled ladies—ever rose to the surface in print before the nineteenth century. Then, what a change could be seen. A woman, indeed, Elizabeth Browning, was one of the strongest candidates for the Laureateship in 1850. Many names just survive now in older anthologies or the words of songs, but a very few outlived all changes in fashion to hold an absolute place in the roll of poets today. Mrs Browning would count as one, but she is probably now less esteemed than the two other leading women poets of her time: Emily Brontë and Christina Rossetti. The American Emily Dickinson may have been the most remarkable poet of all. But she simply was not known in the England of her day.

Christina Rossetti was born in London on December 5th, 1830; she was the youngest of four—all arriving within four years—of a lively, talented half-Italian family. One could say that from this time and setting sprang most of the good and bad fortune in her story. As a child with a gift for writing, she grew up in a home full of encouragement. The young Rossettis ran their own magazines, set each other literary projects (like composing sonnets to given end-rhymes), throve on each other's criticism, and were thoroughly practised poets, skilled in technical subtleties, by the time they reached their teens. ('Spring Quiet' on p. 34—a poem much less simple than it may seem—was one of these youthful works.) One thinks of the four Brontë children, born an exact decade earlier, learning their craft with an even greater intensity, in the north.

5

But, childhood over, Christina became an adult in mid-Victorian England—a wretched time not only for the poor and for animals but for nearly all women, with its crippling and irrational laws and conventions, and its absence of almost any worthwhile chance of work. To complicate matters, she came from a family with two contradictory creeds. The atheistical father had fought all his life for political and religious liberty; the Anglican mother was no less conforming, and strictly devout. Maria and Christina Rossetti accepted their mother's beliefs; the result was to mark almost every turn in their lives. But the boys, like their father, declared themselves freethinkers, a daring view at a time when shades of religious observance caused far more angry feeling and anguished decision than any matter of politics or social reform.

To understand the atmosphere of Christina's home, we should know something more of the parents. Gabriele Rossetti, the father, had come to England in 1824 as a political refugee. In Naples he had been a popular poet and a leading patriot-figure in the Republican underground. He was even, briefly, a member of the government before the Bourbons regained the shaky Neapolitan throne in 1821, and Rossetti's exile (by way of Malta) began. Settling in England, he married Miss Frances Polidori, a young English governess, and so the young Rossettis came to be born.

But Frances herself was the daughter of an unconventional Italian father and a strictly religious English mother. Her wild brother John Polidori (still remembered as Byron's travelling physician) was considered the family disgrace for his 'dissolute' ways; he finally took his own life at the age of twenty-six. On the other hand, her two older sisters, Christina's aunts, were orderly characters, successfully working as governesses. One of them taught the Marchioness of Bath's young family at Longleat; later, she stayed on as 'companion'. Christina would sometimes visit her aunt in this splendid place.

A vivid account of the Rossettis' childhood home comes

from Christina's brother, William Michael. Their Blooms-
bury house seemed always full of Italian visitors—

'exiles, patriots, politicians, literary men, musicians;
fleshy good-natured Neapolitans, keen Tuscans, emphatic
Romans. As we children were habituated from our earliest
years to speaking Italian with our father, we were able to
follow all or most of the speech of these "natives"; and a
conspirator or a semi-brigand might present himself, and
open out on his topics of predilection, without our being
told to leave the room. All this . . . made us, no doubt, not
a little different from British children.'

Sometimes, he adds, talk on 'affairs of Europe' might alternate
with 'fervent recitals of poetry'; the mother would sit there—

'quiet but interested, sometimes taking her mild womanly
part in the conversation; and we four children . . .
drinking it all in as a sort of necessary atmosphere of the
daily life, yet with our own little interests and occupations
as well—reading, colouring prints, looking into illustrated
books, nursing a cat, or whatever came uppermost.'

The children had decided tastes in their own entertainments;
in reading, for instance, they detested pious and moralising
books, like *Sandford and Merton*, but they never tired of fairy
tales, the *Arabian Nights*, and any stories of demons, ghosts
and witches. At nine, Christina discovered a wonderful
poem, 'The Eve of St Agnes' by Keats, a poet not long dead
and not yet the world-famed classic that he has since become.
We hear of them visiting Madame Tussaud's and the Zoo in
Regent's Park (Christina's fondness for animals, reflected in
her poems, extended to bats, moths, beetles, toads and mice).
There were glorious summer visits to grandfather Polidori's
country cottage in Buckinghamshire, where Christina had, as
she later wrote, 'the delightful idle liberty to prowl all alone
about the cottage-grounds . . . The grounds were quite
small, and on the simplest scale—but in those days to me they
were vast, varied and worth exploring.'

The four Rossettis never lost their clannish loyalty, and

7

their interest, however teasingly critical, in one another's work. But their lives were to take different paths. Because of their father's long and serious illness, Maria became a governess at seventeen, and fifteen-year-old William Michael a clerk in the Excise Office. Maria, though a clever and vigorous-minded girl, had, unfairly, little share of the family's good looks and inventive gifts; her happiest time was near the end of her life when she became a nun in an Anglican order. Dante Gabriel, most brilliant of the family, was to make a lasting impact on English painting and poetry, not only through his actual work but through his ideas and personality. He was not much more than twenty when he became the leading spirit of the new Pre-Raphaelite movement. A genuine London bohemian of the mid-century, he was, certainly, a picturesque character, especially when seen at a distance. As a poet, he was even more remarkable than as a painter, though it was by his painting that he lived. But drug-taking and other hazards destroyed him before his end; he died after years of nightmarish mental and physical illness, in 1882.

William Michael was the dependable one. True, he held atheistic views, but he worked responsibly in the Civil Service, and helped to support all the rest of the family as long as the need remained. He outlived them all by many a year (surviving, in fact, until 1919). The big volume of Christina Rossetti's collected poems was one of his quiet achievements; the Memoir at the beginning (an indispensable source for anyone writing about the Rossettis) shows, too, that this self-effacing brother had no small literary ability himself. His account is discreet yet penetrating; he can make his affectionate praise seem also appraisal, an assessment perfectly judged. He married Lucy, the daughter of the Pre-Raphaelite painter Ford Madox Brown, and through their children the Rossetti line continues today.

What became of Christina? She had been a wilful, pretty, spirited little girl, ranked second to Gabriel in gifts and looks—and in temper, too. (She and Gabriel were known as

'the storms', Maria and William Michael as 'the calms'.)
Now we find her a pensive, reserved, mysterious girl, beauti-
ful rather than pretty, with a smooth pale olive-coloured
skin, clear-cut delicate features, heavy-lidded eyes, unsmiling,
curving lips. So we can see her, time and again, in her brother
Gabriel's exquisite sketches, in the paintings for which he
used her as model ('The Girlhood of Mary Virgin', for
instance), even in photographs; it is a secret face, noble and
dreaming, like that of an angel in an old Italian painting. It
is also oddly passionate.

But in life, the secret, passionate angel was a Victorian
gentlewoman; one, moreover, of strict religious principles.
Still, she took what choice she could, and, having no wish to
be a governess, she stayed at home. We hear of her, at
twenty-four, making a mild, improbable attempt to join one
of her enterprising Polidori aunts as a nurse with Miss
Nightingale at Scutari. Imagination refuses to follow this
picture further. She met her brothers' Pre-Raphaelite
friends, and wrote for their magazine. Twice, she was
engaged to be married and twice withdrew, supposedly on
religious grounds. (The first of her suitors wavered in and
out of the Roman Catholic Church; the second, Charles
Cayley, a more congenial character, was inclined to no
Church at all.) But a likelier reason could have been that
marriage had far less interest for her than romantic love, and
this she did not feel for either young man—though the
agnostic Cayley remained to the last a comfortable friend.
Her latest biographer suggests that she did find elsewhere a
more intense (if unfulfilled) relationship which accounts for
the heights and depths of her many poems on love.

> At length there came the step upon the stair,
>   Upon the lock the old familiar hand:
> Then first my spirit seemed to scent the air
>   Of Paradise; then first the tardy sand
> Of time ran golden; and I felt my hair
>   Put on a glory, and my soul expand.

9

It could account, too, for the recurring theme of meeting and parting in her work.

> To meet, worth living for;
> Worth dying for, to meet;
> To meet, worth parting for:
> Bitter forgot in sweet.

Her poems seem often written about the immediate day's experiences. Indeed, set down as they usually are in note-books (a mounting pile as the years went on, with the day's date on each), they are the closest record we have of her enigmatic life. The answers to the clues can only be guessed at. But the experiences can be felt by all who read.

Christina's most important and most original work is one unlike nearly everything else that she wrote—her richly colourful story-poem 'Goblin Market'. The opening lines are in this selection, but anyone who does not know the whole poem, and who feels at all interested in the Pre-Raphaelites, should hunt it up and read it through straight away. It tells of two girls whom a troop of goblins daily try to tempt with their evil, alluring fruits. One resists ('Who knows upon what soil they fed/Their hungry thirsty roots?'); one does not—with terrible results. At last, the second girl goes out herself to the goblin den to save her sister.

Children have always read this as a rhyming fairy tale; adults have seen in it all kinds of allegorical meanings. We can take it as we will. But a further point that might interest us now is that in its time its style was thought too 'advanced' for many tastes; its metres were too unconventional; it used unpoetic words. 'Lugs', for instance, ('One hauls a basket, One lugs a golden dish') was much objected to.

But most of her poetry takes a shorter, lyrical, more purely personal form. It seems on the surface as clear as water, but the water is deep, with unsuspected tides. These lyrical poems grow out of stillness as much as action, out of solitude, not society. Sometimes they hint at a story; 'Winter: My Secret' (p. 48), for instance, certainly does. But even in this unusually high-spirited poem, the mystery stays in the air. And though we do find moods of ecstatic delight in her verse, the prevailing note is one of a haunting sadness. Sometimes she seems oppressively self-tormenting and resigned. Yet, again, her poems of loss or longing can have a thrilling poignancy that stirs us as much as joy.

> Somewhere or other there must surely be
> The face not seen, the voice not heard,
> The heart that not yet—never yet—ah me!
> Made answer to my word.

It is curious to see, though, how little outward life is reflected in Christina Rossetti's poems. You could guess a good deal from their work about Elizabeth Browning's world, or Emily Dickinson's, or even Emily Brontë's. Christina was London-born, and lived in London nearly all of her days. But there is nothing to give any clue to this in her verse; no hint of the houses, the gas-lit streets, crossing sweepers and carriages. There is nothing of Longleat or of her two Continental journeys. An interesting sonnet (not given here) does, however, describe her brother's studio ('One face looks out from all his canvases'). Her childhood visits to the country did much, she said, to make her into a poet—but it was not landscape that she remembered. Her most vivid personal observation was of the small living creatures and plants that a child's eye might perceive—not only birds (as in the lovely poem 'A Green Cornfield' on p. 26), but insects and other unlikely animals. Some of these can be found in 'Twilight Calm' on p. 20.

Even the sea and the seacoast are recalled only through this kind of detail—

> Anemones, salt, passionless,
> Blow flowerlike—just enough alive
> To blow and multiply and thrive.
> Shells quaint with curve or spot or spike,
> Encrusted live things argus-eyed,

All fair alike yet all unlike,
Are born without a pang, and die
Without a pang, and so pass by.

In her middle life she wrote a book of nursery verses; it was published under the title *Sing-Song*, with pictures by that prince of illustrators, Arthur Hughes. If any poems in the present selection seem to be written for very young children, the fact is that they were; for they come from that nursery volume. Today we think that it is not necessary to write special verses for young or old; a true poem has something for all readers. But some of the rhymes from *Sing-Song* are well worth sharing with older readers; 'What is pink?' (p. 44), for instance, has always been a favourite.

As she grew older, Christina turned more and more to devotional subjects, and drew more and more on her shadowy inward vision. But her skill remained, and this gives even her sombrest work a living quality. Every craftsman has a unique and personal gift, and Christina's was always of a kind to keep her among the poets. Some may prefer the vision of Emily Brontë or Emily Dickinson, solitaries both in their differing private worlds. But at her best, Christina Rossetti can catch in what seems the lightest possible way some piercing, almost inexpressible idea, and make it seem a revelation of our own unrealised thoughts. And this, after all, is the high achievement of poetry.

Compiler's Note

The only poems of Christina Rossetti now in print—apart from those reproduced in anthologies—are the rhymes for young children, *Sing-Song*, first published in 1872. Some of these are included in my selection (on pp. 28, 29, 30, 31, 38, 44, 53, 54, 55, 56, 57, 58 and 72) and I have given them titles, although originally published without. The text of the poems has been taken from the definitive edition of the poet's work: *The Poetical Works of Christina Georgina Rossetti*, with Memoir and Notes by William Michael Rossetti, published in 1904. Where I have included extracts from longer poems, as on pp. 22, 24, 42, 47, 61, 63 and 81, I have given titles to the extracts, while indicating the title of the whole poem at the end. Where consecutive poems happen to have the same titles (as on pp. 73, 74, 84 and 85) I have replaced these with first-line titles.

D.P.
October, 1969

Contents

BIRDS, BEASTS AND FISHES

TWILIGHT CALM

Oh pleasant eventide!
Clouds on the western side
Grow grey and greyer, hiding the warm sun:
The bees and birds, their happy labours done,
Seek their close nests and bide.

Screened in the leafy wood
The stock-doves sit and brood:
The very squirrel leaps from bough to bough
But lazily; pauses; and settles now
Where once he stored his food.

One by one the flowers close,
Lily and dewy rose
Shutting their tender petals from the moon:
The grasshoppers are still; but not so soon
Are still the noisy crows.

The dormouse squats and eats
Choice little dainty bits
Beneath the spreading roots of a broad lime;
Nibbling his fill he stops from time to time
And listens where he sits.

From far the lowings come
Of cattle driven home;
From farther still the wind brings fitfully
The vast continual murmur of the sea,
Now loud, now almost dumb.

The gnats whirl in the air,
The evening gnats; and there
The owl opes broad his eyes and wings to sail
For prey; the bat wakes; and the shell-less snail
Comes forth, clammy and bare.

Hark! that's the nightingale,
  Telling the self-same tale
Her song told when this ancient earth was young:
So echoes answered when her song was sung
  In the first wooded vale.

We call it love and pain,
  The passion of her strain;
And yet we little understand or know:
Why should it not be rather joy that so
  Throbs in each throbbing vein?

In separate herds the deer
  Lie; here the bucks, and here
The does, and by its mother sleeps the fawn:
Through all the hours of night until the dawn
  They sleep, forgetting fear.

The hare sleeps where it lies,
  With wary half-closed eyes;
The cock has ceased to crow, the hen to cluck:
Only the fox is out, some heedless duck
  Or chicken to surprise.

Remote, each single star
  Comes out, till there they are
All shining brightly. How the dews fall damp!
While close at hand the glow-worm lights her lamp,
  Or twinkles from afar.

But evening now is done
  As much as if the sun
Day-giving had arisen in the East—
For night has come; and the great calm has ceased,
  The quiet sands have run.

OTHER EYES THAN OURS

And other eyes than ours
Were made to look on flowers,
Eyes of small birds and insects small:
The deep sun-blushing rose
Round which the prickles close
Opens her bosom to them all.
The tiniest living thing
That soars on feathered wing,
Or crawls among the long grass out of sight,
Has just as good a right
To its appointed portion of delight
As any King.
(from *To What Purpose Is This Waste?*)

BIRD OR BEAST?

Did any bird come flying
    After Adam and Eve,
When the door was shut against them
    And they sat down to grieve?

I think not Eve's peacock,
    Splendid to see,
And I think not Adam's eagle;
    But a dove maybe.

Did any beast come pushing
    Through the thorny hedge
Into the thorny thistly world,
    Out from Eden's edge?

I think not a lion,
    Though his strength is such;
But an innocent loving lamb
    May have done as much . . .

WHEN CAIN SLEW ABEL

Thus she sat weeping,
Thus Eve our mother,
Where one lay sleeping
Slain by his brother.
Greatest and least
Each piteous beast
To hear her voice
Forgot his joys
And set aside his feast.

The mouse paused in his walk
And dropped his wheaten stalk;
Grave cattle wagged their heads
In rumination;
The eagle gave a cry
From his cloud station;
Larks on thyme beds
Forbore to mount or sing;
Bees drooped upon the wing;
The raven perched on high
Forgot his ration;
The conies in their rock,
A feeble nation,
Quaked sympathetical;
The mocking-bird left off to mock;
Huge camels knelt as if
In deprecation;
The kind hart's tears were falling;
Chattered the wistful stork;
Dove-voices with a dying fall
Cooed desolation,
Answering grief by grief.

Only the serpent in the dust,
Wriggling and crawling,
Grinned an evil grin and thrust
His tongue out with its fork.

(from Eve)

A GREEN CORNFIELD

The earth was green, the sky was blue:
   I saw and heard one sunny morn
A skylark hang between the two,
   A singing speck above the corn;

A stage below, in gay accord,
   White butterflies danced on the wing,
And still the singing skylark soared,
   And silent sank and soared to sing.

The cornfield stretched a tender green
   To right and left beside my walks;
I knew he had a nest unseen
   Somewhere among the million stalks.

And as I paused to hear his song,
   While swift the sunny moments slid,
Perhaps his mate sat listening long,
   And listened longer than I did.

WINTER

Sweet blackbird is silenced with chaffinch and thrush,
Only waistcoated robin still chirps in the bush:
Soft sun-loving swallows have mustered in force,
And winged to the spice-teeming southlands their course.

Plump housekeeper dormouse has tucked himself neat,
Just a brown ball in moss with a morsel to eat:
Armed hedgehog has huddled him into the hedge,
While frogs scarce miss freezing deep down in the sedge.

Soft swallows have left us alone in the lurch,
But robin sits whistling to us from his perch:
If I were red robin, I'd pipe you a tune
Would make you despise all the beauties of June.

But, since that cannot be, let us draw round the fire,
Munch chestnuts, tell stories, and stir the blaze higher:
We'll comfort pinched robin with crumbs, little man,
Till he sings us the very best song that he can.

A LINNET IN A GILDED CAGE

A linnet in a gilded cage,—
A linnet on a bough,—
In frosty winter one might doubt
Which bird is luckier now.

But let the trees burst out in leaf,
And nests be on the bough,—
Which linnet is the luckier bird,
Oh who could doubt it now?

LAMBS AT PLAY

On the grassy banks
Lambkins at their pranks;
Woolly sisters, woolly brothers
Jumping off their feet
While their woolly mothers
Watch by them and bleat.

THE CATERPILLAR

Brown and furry
Caterpillar in a hurry
Take your walk
To the shady leaf, or stalk,
Or what not,
Which may be the chosen spot.
No toad spy you,
Hovering bird of prey pass by you;
Spin and die,
To live again a butterfly.

THE FROG AND THE TOAD

Hopping frog, hop here and be seen,
  I'll not pelt you with stick or stone:
Your cap is laced and your coat is green;
  Good-bye, we'll let each other alone.

Plodding toad, plod here and be looked at,
You the finger of scorn is crooked at:
But though you're lumpish, you're harmless too;
You won't hurt me, and I won't hurt you.

THE CITY MOUSE AND
THE GARDEN MOUSE

The city mouse lives in a house;—
    The garden mouse lives in a bower,
He's friendly with the frogs and toads,
    And sees the pretty plants in flower.

The city mouse eats bread and cheese;—
    The garden mouse eats what he can;
We will not grudge him seeds and stalks,
    Poor little timid furry man.

A MOTHERLESS SOFT LAMBKIN

A motherless soft lambkin
    Alone upon a hill;
No mother's fleece to shelter him
    And wrap him from the cold:—
I'll run to him and comfort him,
    I'll fetch him, that I will;
I'll care for him and feed him
    Until he's strong and bold.

HORSES

The horses of the sea
  Rear a foaming crest,
But the horses of the land
  Serve us the best.

The horses of the land
  Munch corn and clover,
While the foaming sea-horses
  Toss and turn over.

HURT NO LIVING THING

Hurt no living thing:
  Ladybird, nor butterfly,
Nor moth with dusty wing,
  Nor cricket chirping cheerily,
Nor grasshopper so light of leap,
  Nor dancing gnat, nor beetle fat,
Nor harmless worms that creep.

OUT OF DOORS

SPRING QUIET

Gone were but the Winter,
  Come were but the Spring,
I would go to a covert
  Where the birds sing;

Where in the whitethorn
  Singeth a thrush,
And a robin sings
  In the holly-bush.

Full of fresh scents
  Are the budding boughs
Arching high over
  A cool green house;

Full of sweet scents,
  And whispering air
Which sayeth softly:
  'We spread no snare;

'Here dwell in safety,
  Here dwell alone,
With a clear stream
  And a mossy stone.

'Here the sun shineth
  Most shadily;
Here is heard an echo
  Of the far sea,
  Though far off it be.'

THE FIRST SPRING DAY

I wonder if the sap is stirring yet,
If wintry birds are dreaming of a mate,
If frozen snowdrops feel as yet the sun
And crocus fires are kindling one by one:
   Sing, robin, sing;
I still am sore in doubt concerning Spring.

I wonder if the Springtide of this year
Will bring another Spring both lost and dear;
If heart and spirit will find out their Spring,
Or if the world alone will bud and sing:
   Sing, hope, to me;
Sweet notes, my hope, soft notes for memory.

The sap will surely quicken soon or late,
The tardiest bird will twitter to a mate;
So Spring must dawn again with warmth and bloom,
Or in this world or in the world to come:
   Sing, voice of Spring,
Till I too blossom and rejoice and sing.

SPRING

Frost-locked all the winter,
Seeds, and roots, and stones of fruits,
What shall make their sap ascend
That they may put forth shoots?
Tips of tender green,
Leaf, or blade, or sheath;
Telling of the hidden life
That breaks forth underneath,
Life nursed in its grave by Death.

Blows the thaw-wind pleasantly,
Drips the soaking rain,
By fits looks down the waking sun:
Young grass springs on the plain;
Young leaves clothe early hedgerow trees;
Seeds, and roots, and stones of fruits,
Swoln with sap put forth their shoots;
Curled-headed ferns sprout in the lane;
Birds sing and pair again.

There is no time like Spring,
When life's alive in everything,
Before new nestlings sing,
Before cleft swallows speed their journey back
Along the trackless track—
God guides their wing,
He spreads their table that they nothing lack,—
Before the daisy grows a common flower,
Before the sun has power
To scorch the world up in his noontide hour.

There is no time like Spring,
Like Spring that passes by;
There is no life like Spring-life born to die,—
Piercing the sod,
Clothing the uncouth clod,
Hatched in the nest,
Fledged on the windy bough,
Strong on the wing:
There is no time like Spring that passes by,
Now newly born, and now
Hastening to die.

Minnie and Mattie
  And fat little May,
Out in the country,
  Spending a day.

Such a bright day,
  With the sun glowing,
And the trees half in leaf,
  And the grass growing.

Pinky white pigling
  Squeals through his snout,
Woolly white lambkin
  Frisks all about.

Cluck! cluck! the nursing hen
  Summons her folk,—
Ducklings all downy soft,
  Yellow as yolk.

Cluck! cluck! the mother hen
  Summons her chickens
To peck the dainty bits
  Found in her pickings.

Minnie and Mattie
  And May carry posies,
Half of sweet violets,
  Half of primroses.

Give the sun time enough,
  Glowing and glowing,
He'll rouse the roses
  And bring them blowing.

Don't wait for roses,
   Losing today,
O Minnie, Mattie,
   And wise little May.

Violets and primroses
   Blossom today
For Minnie and Mattie
   And fat little May.

MAY

I cannot tell you how it was;
But this I know: it came to pass—
Upon a bright and breezy day
When May was young, ah pleasant May!
As yet the poppies were not born
Between the blades of tender corn;
The last eggs had not hatched as yet,
Nor any bird forgone its mate.

I cannot tell you what it was;
But this I know: it did but pass.
It passed away with sunny May,
With all sweet things it passed away,
And left me old, and cold, and grey.

IMMALEE

I gather thyme upon the sunny hills,
  And its pure fragrance ever gladdens me,
  And in my mind having tranquillity
I smile to see how my green basket fills.
And by clear streams I gather daffodils;
  And in dim woods find out the cherry-tree,
  And take its fruit and the wild strawberry
And nuts and honey; and live free from ills.
I dwell on the green earth, 'neath the blue sky,
  Birds are my friends, and leaves my rustling roof:
The deer are not afraid of me, and I
  Hear the wild goat, and hail its hastening hoof;
The squirrels sit perked as I pass them by,
  And even the watchful hare stands not aloof.

COME BUY, COME BUY

Morning and evening
Maids heard the goblins cry:
'Come buy our orchard fruits,
Come buy, come buy:
Apples and quinces,
Lemons and oranges,
Plump unpecked cherries,
Melons and raspberries,
Bloom-down-cheeked peaches,
Swart-headed mulberries,
Wild free-born cranberries,
Crab-apples, dewberries,
Pine-apples, blackberries,
Apricots, strawberries;—
All ripe together
In summer weather,—
Morns that pass by,
Fair eves that fly;
Come buy, come buy:
Our grapes fresh from the vine,
Pomegranates full and fine,
Dates and sharp bullaces,
Rare pears and greengages,
Damsons and bilberries,
Taste them and try:
Currants and gooseberries,
Bright-fire-like barberries,
Figs to fill your mouth,
Citrons from the South,
Sweet to tongue and sound to eye;
Come buy, come buy.'

(from *Goblin Market*)

SUMMER

Winter is cold-hearted,
Spring is yea and nay,
Autumn is a weathercock
    Blown every way.
    Summer days for me
When every leaf is on its tree;

When Robin's not a beggar,
And Jenny Wren's a bride,
And larks hang singing, singing, singing,
    Over the wheat-fields wide,
    And anchored lilies ride,
    And the pendulum spider
    Swings from side to side;

And blue-black beetles transact business,
    And gnats fly in a host,
And furry caterpillars hasten
    That no time be lost,
    And moths grow fat and thrive,
    And ladybirds arrive.

Before green apples blush,
    Before green nuts embrown,
    Why, one day in the country
    Is worth a month in town;
    Is worth a day and a year
Of the dusty, musty, lag-last fashion
    That days drone elsewhere.

GOLDEN GLORIES

The buttercup is like a golden cup,
  The marigold is like a golden frill,
The daisy with a golden eye looks up,
  And golden spreads the flag beside the rill,
  And gay and golden nods the daffodil;
The gorsy common swells a golden sea,
  The cowslip hangs a head of golden tips,
And golden drips the honey which the bee
  Sucks from sweet hearts of flowers and stores and sips.

WHAT IS PINK?

What is pink? a rose is pink
By the fountain's brink.
What is red? a poppy's red
In its barley bed.
What is blue? the sky is blue
Where the clouds float through.
What is white? a swan is white
Sailing in the light.
What is yellow? pears are yellow,
Rich and ripe and mellow.
What is green? the grass is green,
With small flowers between.
What is violet? clouds are violet
In the summer twilight.
What is orange? why, an orange,
Just an orange!

THE ROSE

O Rose, thou flower of flowers, thou fragrant wonder,
  Who shall describe thee in thy ruddy prime,
  Thy perfect fullness in the summertime,
When the pale leaves blushingly part asunder
And show the warm red heart lies glowing under?
  Thou shouldst bloom surely in some sunny clime,
  Untouched by blights and chilly winter's rime,
Where lightnings never flash nor peals the thunder.
And yet in happier spheres they cannot need thee
  So much as we do with our weight of woe;
Perhaps they would not tend, perhaps not heed thee,
  And thou wouldst lonely and neglected grow;
And He who is all wise, He hath decreed thee
  To gladden earth and cheer all hearts below.

SEASONS

Crocuses and snowdrops wither,
Violets, primroses together,
Fading with the fading Spring
Before a fuller blossoming.

O sweet Summer, pass not soon,
Stay awhile the harvest-moon:
O sweetest Summer, do not go,
For Autumn's next and next the snow.

When Autumn comes the days are drear,
It is the downfall of the year:
We heed the wind and falling leaf
More than the golden harvest-sheaf.

Dreary Winter come at last:
Come quickly, so be quickly past:
Dusk and sluggish Winter, wane
Till Spring and sunlight dawn again.

OCTOBER

I've brought you nuts and hops;
And when the leaf drops, why, the walnut drops.
Crack your first nut and light your first fire,
　Roast your first chestnut crisp on the bar;
Make the logs sparkle, stir the blaze higher,
　Logs are cheery as sun or as star,
　Logs we can find wherever we are.

Spring one soft day will open the leaves,
　Spring one bright day will lure back the flowers;
Never fancy my whistling wind grieves,
　Never fancy I've tears in my showers:
　Dance, nights and days! and dance on, my hours!
(from The Months)

WINTER: MY SECRET

I tell my secret? No indeed, not I:
Perhaps some day, who knows?
But not today; it froze, and blows, and snows,
And you're too curious: fie!
You want to hear it? well:
Only, my secret's mine, and I won't tell.

Or, after all, perhaps there's none:
Suppose there is no secret after all,
But only just my fun.
Today's a nipping day, a biting day,
In which one wants a shawl,
A veil, a cloak, and other wraps:
I cannot ope to every one who taps,
And let the draughts come whistling through my hall;
Come bounding and surrounding me,
Come buffeting, astounding me,
Nipping and clipping through my wraps and all.
I wear my mask for warmth: who ever shows
His nose to Russian snows
To be pecked at by every wind that blows?
You would not peck? I thank you for good will,
Believe, but leave that truth untested still.

Spring's an expansive time: yet I don't trust
March with its peck of dust,
Nor April with its rainbow-crowned brief showers,
Nor even May, whose flowers
One frost may wither through the sunless hours.

Perhaps some languid summer day,
When drowsy birds sing less and less,
And golden fruit is ripening to excess,
If there's not too much sun nor too much cloud,
And the warm wind is neither still nor loud,
Perhaps my secret I may say,
Or you may guess.

WINTER RAIN

Every valley drinks,
  Every dell and hollow;
Where the kind rain sinks and sinks,
  Green of Spring will follow.

Yet a lapse of weeks—
  Buds will burst their edges,
Strip their wool-coats, glue-coats, streaks,
  In the woods and hedges;

Weave a bower of love
  For birds to meet each other,
Weave a canopy above
  Nest and egg and mother.

But for fattening rain
  We should have no flowers,
Never a bud or leaf again
  But for soaking showers;

Never a mated bird
  In the rocking tree-tops,
Never indeed a flock or herd
  To graze upon the lea-crops.

Lambs so woolly white,
  Sheep the sun-bright leas on,
They could have no grass to bite
  But for rain in season.

We should find no moss
  In the shadiest places,
Find no waving meadow grass
  Pied with broad-eyed daisies:

But miles of barren sand,
　With never a son or daughter;
Not a lily on the land,
　Or lily on the water.

BY THE WATER

There are rivers lapsing down
   Lily-laden to the sea:
Every lily is a boat
   For bees, one, two, or three:
I wish there were a fairy boat
   For you, my friend, and me.

And if there were a fairy boat
   And if the river bore us,
We should not care for all the past
   Nor all that lies before us,
Not for the hopes that buoyed us once,
   Not for the fears that tore us.

We would rock upon the river
   Scarcely floating by,
Rocking, rocking like the lilies,
   You, my friend, and I;
Rocking like the stately lilies
   Beneath the statelier sky.

But ah where is that river
   Whose hyacinth banks descend
Down to the sweeter lilies
   Till soft their shadows blend
Into a watery twilight?—
   And ah where is my friend?

THE SOUND OF THE WIND

The wind has such a rainy sound
  Moaning through the town,
The sea has such a windy sound,—
  Will the ships go down?

The apples in the orchard
  Tumble from their tree.—
Oh will the ships go down, go down,
  In the windy sea?

THE FERRYMAN

'Ferry me across the water,
   Do, boatman, do.'
'If you've a penny in your purse
   I'll ferry you.'

'I have a penny in my purse,
   And my eyes are blue;
So ferry me across the water,
   Do, boatman, do.'

'Step into my ferry-boat,
   Be they black or blue,
And for the penny in your purse
   I'll ferry you.'

THE WIND

Who has seen the wind?
  Neither I nor you:
But when the leaves hang trembling,
  The wind is passing through.

Who has seen the wind?
  Neither you nor I:
But when the trees bow down their heads,
  The wind is passing by.

*   *   *

O wind, why do you never rest,
  Wandering, whistling to and fro,
Bringing rain out of the west,
  From the dim north bringing snow?

BOATS SAIL ON THE RIVERS

Boats sail on the rivers,
  And ships sail on the seas;
But clouds that sail across the sky
  Are prettier far than these.

There are bridges on the rivers,
  As pretty as you please;
But the bow that bridges heaven,
  And overtops the trees,
And builds a road from earth to sky,
  Is prettier far than these.

CORAL

O sailor, come ashore,
　　What have you brought for me?
Red coral, white coral,
　　Coral from the sea.

I did not dig it from the ground,
　　Nor pluck it from a tree;
Feeble insects made it
　　In the stormy sea.

THE FLINT

An emerald is as green as grass;
　　A ruby red as blood;
A sapphire shines as blue as heaven;
　　A flint lies in the mud.

A diamond is a brilliant stone,
　　To catch the world's desire;
An opal holds a fiery spark;
　　But a flint holds fire.

THE MOON

Is the moon tired? she looks so pale
Within her misty veil:
She scales the sky from east to west,
And takes no rest.

Before the coming of the night
The moon shows papery white;
Before the dawning of the day
She fades away.

*   *   *

If the moon came from heaven,
   Talking all the way,
What could she have to tell us,
   And what could she say?

'I've seen a hundred pretty things,
   And seen a hundred gay;
But only think: I peep by night
   And do not peep by day!'

*   *   *

O Lady Moon, your horns point toward the east;
   Shine, be increased:
O Lady Moon, your horns point toward the west;
   Wane, be at rest.

LOVE HUMAN AND DIVINE

A PAUSE

They made the chamber sweet with flowers and leaves,
  And the bed sweet with flowers on which I lay;
  While my soul, love-bound, loitered on its way.
I did not hear the birds about the eaves,
Nor hear the reapers talk among the sheaves:
  Only my soul kept watch from day to day,
  My thirsty soul kept watch for one away:—
Perhaps he loves, I thought, remembers, grieves.
At length there came the step upon the stair,
  Upon the lock the old familiar hand:
Then first my spirit seemed to scent the air
  Of Paradise; then first the tardy sand
Of time ran golden; and I felt my hair
  Put on a glory, and my soul expand.

BRIDE SONG

Too late for love, too late for joy,
    Too late, too late!
You loitered on the road too long,
    You trifled at the gate:
The enchanted dove upon her branch
    Died without a mate;
The enchanted princess in her tower
    Slept, died, behind the grate;
Her heart was starving all this while
    You made it wait.

Ten years ago, five years ago,
    One year ago,
Even then you had arrived in time,
    Though somewhat slow;
Then you had known her living face
    Which now you cannot know:
The frozen fountain would have leaped,
    The buds gone on to blow,
The warm south wind would have awaked
    To melt the snow.

Is she fair now as she lies?
    Once she was fair;
Meet queen for any kingly king,
    With gold-dust on her hair.
Now these are poppies in her locks,
    White poppies she must wear;
Must wear a veil to shroud her face
    And the want graven there:
Or is the hunger fed at length,
    Cast off the care?

We never saw her with a smile
   Or with a frown;
Her bed seemed never soft to her,
   Though tossed of down;
She little heeded what she wore,
   Kirtle, or wreath, or gown;
We think her white brows often ached
   Beneath her crown,
Till silvery hairs showed in her locks
   That used to be so brown.

We never heard her speak in haste;
   Her tones were sweet,
And modulated just so much
   As it was meet:
Her heart sat silent through the noise
   And concourse of the street.
There was no hurry in her hands,
   No hurry in her feet;
There was no bliss drew nigh to her,
   That she might run to greet.

You should have wept her yesterday,
   Wasting upon her bed:
But wherefore should you weep today
   That she is dead?
Lo, we who love weep not today,
   But crown her royal head.
Let be these poppies that we strew,
   Your roses are too red:
Let be these poppies, not for you
   Cut down and spread.
         (from *The Prince's Progress*)

THAT FIRST DAY

I wish I could remember that first day,
   First hour, first moment of your meeting me,
   If bright or dim the season, it might be
Summer or Winter for aught I can say;
So unrecorded did it slip away,
   So blind was I to see and to foresee,
   So dull to mark the budding of my tree
That would not blossom yet for many a May.
If only I could recollect it, such
   A day of days! I let it come and go
   As traceless as a thaw of bygone snow;
It seemed to mean so little, meant so much;
If only now I could recall that touch,
   First touch of hand in hand—Did one but know!

(from *Monna Innominata*)

DREAM-LOVE

Young Love lies sleeping
  In May-time of the year,
Among the lilies,
  Lapped in the tender light:
White lambs come grazing,
  White doves come building there;
And round about him
  The May-bushes are white.

Soft moss the pillow
  For oh a softer cheek;
Broad leaves cast shadow
  Upon the heavy eyes:
There winds and waters
  Grow lulled and scarcely speak;
There twilight lingers
  The longest in the skies.

Young Love lies dreaming;
  But who shall tell the dream?
A perfect sunlight
  On rustling forest tips;
Or perfect moonlight
  Upon a rippling stream;
Or perfect silence,
  Or song of cherished lips.

Burn odours round him
  To fill the drowsy air;
Weave silent dances
  Around him to and fro;
For oh in waking
  The sights are not so fair,
And song and silence
  Are not like these below.

Young Love lies dreaming
  Till summer days are gone,—
Dreaming and drowsing
  Away to perfect sleep:
He sees the beauty
  Sun hath not looked upon,
And tastes the fountain
  Unutterably deep.

Him perfect music
  Doth hush unto his rest,
And through the pauses
  The perfect silence calms:
Oh poor the voices
  Of earth from east to west,
And poor earth's stillness
  Between her stately palms!

Young Love lies drowsing
  Away to poppied death;
Cool shadows deepen
  Across the sleeping face:
So fails the summer
  With warm delicious breath;
And what hath autumn
  To give us in its place?

Draw close the curtains
  Of branchèd evergreen;
Change cannot touch them
  With fading fingers sere:
Here the first violets
  Perhaps will bud unseen,
And a dove, maybe,
  Return to nestle here.

ECHO

Come to me in the silence of the night;
  Come in the speaking silence of a dream;
Come with soft rounded cheeks and eyes as bright
   As sunlight on a stream;
    Come back in tears,
O memory, hope, love of finished years.

O dream how sweet, too sweet, too bitter sweet,
  Whose wakening should have been in Paradise,
Where souls brimfull of love abide and meet;
   Where thirsting longing eyes
    Watch the slow door
That opening, letting in, lets out no more.

Yet come to me in dreams, that I may live
  My very life again though cold in death:
Come back to me in dreams, that I may give
   Pulse for pulse, breath for breath:
    Speak low, lean low,
As long ago, my love, how long ago.

A BIRTHDAY

My heart is like a singing bird
  Whose nest is in a watered shoot:
My heart is like an apple-tree
  Whose boughs are bent with thickset fruit;
My heart is like a rainbow shell
  That paddles in a halcyon sea;
My heart is gladder than all these
  Because my love is come to me.

Raise me a dais of silk and down;
  Hang it with vair and purple dyes;
Carve it in doves and pomegranates,
  And peacocks with a hundred eyes;
Work it in gold and silver grapes,
  In leaves and silver fleurs-de-lys;
Because the birthday of my life
  Is come, my love is come to me.

SOMEWHERE OR OTHER

Somewhere or other there must surely be
   The face not seen, the voice not heard,
The heart that not yet—never yet—ah me!
   Made answer to my word.

Somewhere or other, may be near or far;
   Past land and sea, clean out of sight;
Beyond the wandering moon, beyond the star
   That tracks her night by night.

Somewhere or other, may be far or near;
   With just a wall, a hedge, between;
With just the last leaves of the dying year
   Fallen on a turf grown green.

A SKETCH

The blindest buzzard that I know
  Does not wear wings to spread and stir:
  Nor does my special mole wear fur,
And grub among the roots below:
He sports a tail indeed, but then
It's to a coat: he's man with men:
  His quill is cut to a pen.

In other points our friend's a mole,
  A buzzard, beyond scope of speech.
  He sees not what's within his reach,
Misreads the part, ignores the whole;
Misreads the part, so reads in vain,
Ignores the whole though patent plain,—
  Misreads both parts again.

My blindest buzzard that I know,
  My special mole, when will you see?
  Oh no, you must not look at me,
There's nothing hid for me to show.
I might show facts as plain as day:
But, since your eyes are blind, you'd say,
  'Where? What?' and turn away.

AN ECHO FROM WILLOW-WOOD

Two gazed into a pool, he gazed and she,
   Not hand in hand, yet heart in heart, I think,
   Pale and reluctant on the water's brink,
As on the brink of parting which must be.
Each eyed the other's aspect, she and he,
   Each felt one hungering heart leap up and sink,
   Each tasted bitterness which both must drink,
There on the brink of life's dividing sea.
Lilies upon the surface, deep below
   Two wistful faces craving each for each,
     Resolute and reluctant without speech:—
A sudden ripple made the faces flow,
   One moment joined, to vanish out of reach:
     So those hearts joined, and ah were parted so.

CONFLUENTS

As rivers seek the sea,
   Much more deep than they,
So my soul seeks thee
   Far away:
As running rivers moan
On their course alone,
   So I moan
   Left alone.

As the delicate rose
   To the sun's sweet strength
Doth herself unclose,
   Breadth and length;
So spreads my heart to thee
Unveiled utterly,
   I to thee
   Utterly.

As morning dew exhales
   Sunwards pure and free
So my spirit fails
   After thee.
As dew leaves not a trace
On the green earth's face;
   I, no trace
   On thy face.

Its goal the river knows,
   Dewdrops find a way,
Sunlight cheers the rose
   In her day:
Shall I, lone sorrow past,
Find thee at the last?
   Sorrow past,
   Thee at last?

CRYING, MY LITTLE ONE

Crying, my little one, footsore and weary?
   Fall asleep, pretty one, warm on my shoulder:
I must tramp on through the winter night dreary,
   While the snow falls on me colder and colder.

You are my one, and I have not another;
   Sleep soft, my darling, my trouble and treasure;
Sleep warm and soft in the arms of your mother,
   Dreaming of pretty things, dreaming of pleasure.

CHRISTMASTIDE

Love came down at Christmas,
   Love all lovely, Love Divine;
Love was born at Christmas,
   Star and angels gave the sign.

Worship we the Godhead,
   Love Incarnate, Love Divine;
Worship we our Jesus:
   But wherewith for sacred sign?

Love shall be our token,
   Love be yours and love be mine,
Love to God and all men,
   Love for plea and gift and sign.

BEFORE THE PALING OF THE STARS

Before the paling of the stars,
 Before the winter morn,
 Before the earliest cock-crow,
Jesus Christ was born:
  Born in a stable,
 Cradled in a manger,
In the world His hands had made
 Born a stranger.

Priest and King lay fast asleep
 In Jerusalem;
Young and old lay fast asleep
 In crowded Bethlehem;
Saint and Angel, ox and ass,
 Kept a watch together,
 Before the Christmas daybreak
 In the winter weather.

Jesus on His Mother's breast
 In the stable cold,
Spotless Lamb of God was He,
 Shepherd of the fold:
Let us kneel with Mary Maid,
 With Joseph bent and hoary,
With Saint and Angel, ox and ass,
 To hail the King of Glory.

IN THE BLEAK MID-WINTER

In the bleak mid-winter
    Frosty wind made moan,
Earth stood hard as iron,
    Water like a stone;
Snow had fallen, snow on snow,
    Snow on snow,
In the bleak mid-winter
    Long ago.

Our God, Heaven cannot hold Him
    Nor earth sustain;
Heaven and earth shall flee away
    When He comes to reign;
In the bleak mid-winter
    A stable-place sufficed
The Lord God Almighty
    Jesus Christ.

Enough for Him, whom cherubim
    Worship night and day,
A breastful of milk
    And a mangerful of hay;
Enough for Him, whom angels
    Fall down before,
The ox and ass and camel
    Which adore.

Angels and archangels
    May have gathered there,
Cherubim and seraphim
    Thronged the air;
But only His mother
    In her maiden bliss
Worshipped the Beloved
    With a kiss.

What can I give Him,
   Poor as I am?
If I were a shepherd
   I would bring a lamb,
If I were a Wise Man
   I would do my part,—
Yet what I can I give Him,
   Give my heart.

GOOD FRIDAY

Am I a stone, and not a sheep,
   That I can stand, O Christ, beneath Thy cross,
   To number drop by drop Thy Blood's slow loss,
And yet not weep?

Not so those women loved
   Who with exceeding grief lamented Thee;
   Not so fallen Peter weeping bitterly;
Not so the thief was moved;

Not so the Sun and Moon
   Which hid their faces in a starless sky,
A horror of great darkness at broad noon—
   I, only I.

Yet give not o'er,
   But seek Thy sheep, true Shepherd of the flock;
Greater than Moses, turn and look once more
   And smite a rock.

ANOTHER WORLD THAN THIS

SLEEP AT SEA

Sound the deep waters:—
  Who shall sound that deep?—
Too short the plummet,
  And the watchmen sleep.
Some dream of effort
  Up a toilsome steep;
Some dream of pasture grounds
  For harmless sheep.

White shapes flit to and fro
  From mast to mast;
They feel the distant tempest
  That nears them fast:
Great rocks are straight ahead,
  Great shoals not past;
They shout to one another
  Upon the blast.

Oh soft the streams drop music
  Between the hills,
And musical the birds' nests
  Beside those rills;
The nests are types of home
  Love-hidden from ills,
The nests are types of spirits
  Love-music fills.

So dream the sleepers,
  Each man in his place;
The lightning shows the smile
  Upon each face:
The ship is driving,—driving,—
  It drives apace:
And sleepers smile, and spirits
  Bewail their case.

The lightning glares and reddens
  Across the skies;
It seems but sunset
  To those sleeping eyes.
When did the sun go down
  On such a wise?
From such a sunset
  When shall day arise?

'Wake,' call the spirits:
  But to heedless ears:
They have forgotten sorrows
  And hopes and fears;
They have forgotten perils
  And smiles and tears;
Their dream has held them long,
  Long years and years.

'Wake,' call the spirits again:
  But it would take
A louder summons
  To bid them awake.
Some dream of pleasure
  For another's sake:
Some dream, forgetful
  Of a lifelong ache.

One by one slowly,
  Ah how sad and slow!
Wailing and praying
  The spirits rise and go:
Clear stainless spirits,
  White, as white as snow;
Pale spirits, wailing
  For an overthrow.

One by one flitting,
  Like a mournful bird
Whose song is tired at last
  For no mate heard.
The loving voice is silent,
  The useless word;
One by one flitting,
  Sick with hope deferred.

Driving and driving,
  The ship drives amain:
While swift from mast to mast
  Shapes flit again,
Flit silent as the silence
  Where men lie slain;
Their shadow cast upon the sails
  Is like a stain.

No voice to call the sleepers,
  No hand to raise:
They sleep to death in dreaming
  Of length of days.
Vanity of vanities,
  The Preacher says:
Vanity is the end
  Of all their ways.

PASSING AWAY

Passing away, saith the World, passing away:
Chances, beauty, and youth sapped day by day:
Thy life never continueth in one stay.
Is the eye waxen dim, is the dark hair changing to grey
That hath won neither laurel nor bay?
I shall clothe myself in Spring and bud in May:
Thou, root-stricken, shalt not rebuild thy decay
On my bosom for aye.
Then I answered: Yea.

Passing away, saith my Soul, passing away:
With its burden of fear and hope, of labour and play,
Hearken what the past doth witness and say:
Rust in thy gold, a moth is in thine array,
A canker is in thy bud, thy leaf must decay.
At midnight, at cock-crow, at morning, one certain day,
Lo, the Bridegroom shall come and shall not delay:
Watch thou and pray.
Then I answered: Yea.

Passing away, saith my God, passing away:
Winter passeth after the long delay:
New grapes on the vine, new figs on the tender spray,
Turtle calleth turtle in Heaven's May.
Though I tarry, wait for Me, trust Me, watch and pray:
Arise, come away, night is past and lo, it is day;
My love, My sister, My spouse, thou shalt hear Me say.
Then I answered: Yea.

(from *Old and New Year Ditties*)

BIRDS OF PARADISE

Golden-winged, silver-winged,
  Winged with flashing flame,
Such a flight of birds I saw,
  Birds without a name:
Singing songs in their own tongue—
  Song of songs—they came.

One to another calling,
  Each answering each,
One to another calling
In their proper speech:
High above my head they wheeled,
  Far out of reach.

On wings of flame they went and came
  With a cadenced clang:
Their silver wings tinkled,
  Their golden wings rang;
The wind it whistled through their wings
  Where in heaven they sang.

They flashed and they darted
  Awhile before mine eyes,
Mounting, mounting, mounting still,
  In haste to scale the skies,
Birds without a nest on earth,
  Birds of Paradise.

Where the moon riseth not
Nor sun seeks the west,
There to sing their glory
Which they sing at rest,
There to sing their love-song
When they sing their best:—

Not in any garden
  That mortal foot hath trod,
Not in any flowering tree
  That springs from earthly sod,
But in the garden where they dwell,
  The Paradise of God.

SHE SAT AND SANG ALWAY

She sat and sang alway
  By the green margin of a stream,
Watching the fishes leap and play
  Beneath the glad sunbeam.

I sat and wept alway
  Beneath the moon's most shadowy beam,
Watching the blossoms of the May
  Weep leaves into the stream.

I wept for memory;
  She sang for hope that is so fair:
My tears were swallowed by the sea;
  Her songs died on the air.

WHEN I AM DEAD

When I am dead, my dearest,
  Sing no sad songs for me;
Plant thou no roses at my head,
  Nor shady cypress tree:
Be the green grass above me
  With showers and dewdrops wet;
And if thou wilt, remember,
  And if thou wilt, forget.

I shall not see the shadows,
  I shall not feel the rain;
I shall not hear the nightingale
  Sing on as if in pain;
And dreaming through the twilight
  That doth not rise nor set,
Haply I may remember,
  And haply may forget.

OH ROSES FOR THE FLUSH OF YOUTH

Oh roses for the flush of youth,
  And laurel for the perfect prime;
But pluck an ivy branch for me
  Grown old before my time.

Oh violets for the grave of youth,
  And bay for those dead in their prime;
Give me the withered leaves I chose
  Before in the old time.

DREAM LAND

Where sunless rivers weep
Their waves into the deep,
She sleeps a charmèd sleep:
   Awake her not.
Led by a single star,
She came from very far
To seek where shadows are
   Her pleasant lot.

She left the rosy morn,
She left the fields of corn,
For twilight cold and lorn
   And water springs.
Through sleep, as through a veil,
She sees the sky look pale,
And hears the nightingale
   That sadly sings.

Rest, rest, a perfect rest
Shed over brow and breast;
Her face is toward the west,
   The purple land.
She cannot see the grain
Ripening on hill and plain,
She cannot feel the rain
   Upon her hand.

Rest, rest, for evermore
Upon a mossy shore;
Rest, rest at the heart's core
   Till time shall cease:
Sleep that no pain shall wake;
Night that no morn shall break,
Till joy shall overtake
   Her perfect peace.

REST

O Earth, lie heavily upon her eyes;
   Seal her sweet eyes weary of watching, Earth;
   Lie close around her; leave no room for mirth
With its harsh laughter, nor for sound of sighs.
She hath no questions, she hath no replies,
   Hushed in and curtained with a blessèd dearth
   Of all that irked her from the hour of birth;
With stillness that is almost Paradise.
Darkness more clear than noonday holdeth her,
   Silence more musical than any song;
Even her very heart has ceased to stir:
Until the morning of Eternity
Her rest shall not begin nor end, but be;
   And when she wakes she will not think it long.

THE BOURNE

Underneath the growing grass,
    Underneath the living flowers,
    Deeper than the sound of showers:
    There we shall not count the hours
By the shadows as they pass.

Youth and health will be but vain,
    Beauty reckoned of no worth:
    There a very little girth
    Can hold round what once the earth
Seemed too narrow to contain.

FATA MORGANA

A blue-eyed phantom far before
    Is laughing, leaping toward the sun:
Like lead I chase it evermore,
    I pant and run.

It breaks the sunlight bound on bound:
    Goes singing as it leaps along
To sheep-bells with a dreamy sound,
    A dreamy song.

I laugh, it is so brisk and gay;
    It is so far before, I weep:
I hope I shall lie down some day,
    Lie down and sleep.

UPHILL

Does the road wind uphill all the way?
   Yes, to the very end.
Will the day's journey take the whole long day?
   From morn to night, my friend.

But is there for the night a resting-place?
   A roof for when the slow dark hours begin.
May not the darkness hide it from my face?
   You cannot miss that inn.

Shall I meet other wayfarers at night?
   Those who have gone before.
Then must I knock, or call when just in sight?
   They will not keep you standing at that door.

Shall I find comfort, travel-sore and weak?
   Of labour you shall find the sum.
Will there be beds for me and all who seek?
   Yea, beds for all who come.

AMOR MUNDI

'Oh where are you going with your love-locks flowing,
   On the west wind blowing along this valley track?'
'The downhill path is easy, come with me an it please ye,
   We shall escape the uphill by never turning back.'

So they two went together in glowing August weather,
   The honey-breathing heather lay to their left and right;
And dear she was to doat on, her swift feet seemed to float
     on
   The air like soft twin pigeons too sportive to alight.

'Oh what is that in heaven where grey cloud-flakes are
     seven,
   Where blackest clouds hang riven just at the rainy skirt?'
'Oh that's a meteor sent us, a message dumb, portentous,
   An undeciphered solemn signal of help or hurt.'

'Oh what is that glides quickly where velvet flowers grow
     thickly,
   Their scent comes rich and sickly?' 'A scaled and hooded
     worm.'
'Oh what's that in the hollow, so pale I quake to follow?'
   'Oh that's a thin dead body which waits the eternal
     term.'

'Turn again, O my sweetest,—turn again, false and fleetest:
   This beaten way thou beatest, I fear, is hell's own track.'
'Nay, too steep for hill mounting; nay, too late for cost
     counting:
   This downhill path is easy, but there's no turning back.'

A DIRGE

Why were you born when the snow was falling?
You should have come to the cuckoo's calling,
Or when grapes are green in the cluster,
Or at least when lithe swallows muster
  For their far off flying
  From summer dying.

Why did you die when the lambs were cropping?
You should have died at the apples' dropping,
When the grasshopper comes to trouble,
And the wheat-fields are sodden stubble,
  And all winds go sighing
  For sweet things dying.

REMEMBER

Remember me when I am gone away,
  Gone far away into the silent land;
  When you can no more hold me by the hand,
Nor I half turn to go yet turning stay.
Remember me when no more day by day
  You tell me of our future that you plann'd:
  Only remember me; you understand
It will be late to counsel then or pray.
Yet if you should forget me for a while
  And afterwards remember, do not grieve:
  For if the darkness and corruption leave
  A vestige of the thoughts that once I had,
Better by far you should forget and smile
  Than that you should remember and be sad.

SLEEPING AT LAST

Sleeping at last, the trouble and tumult over,
  Sleeping at last, the struggle and horror past,
Cold and white, out of sight of friend and of lover,
    Sleeping at last.

  No more a tired heart downcast or overcast,
No more pangs that wring or shifting fears that hover,
  Sleeping at last in a dreamless sleep locked fast.

Fast asleep. Singing birds in their leafy cover
  Cannot wake her, nor shake her the gusty blast.
Under the purple thyme and the purple clover
    Sleeping at last.

Index of First Lines

95